It's another Quality Book from CGP

This book has been carefully written for Year 5 children
learning science. It's full of questions and investigations
designed to cover the Year 5 objectives on 'Earth and space'
from the latest National Curriculum.

There's also plenty of practice at 'Working Scientifically'
throughout the book.

What CGP is all about

Our sole aim here at CGP is to produce the highest quality books
— carefully written, immaculately presented and
dangerously close to being funny.

Then we work our socks off to get them out to you
— at the cheapest possible prices.

Contents

Section 1 — The Solar System

The Sun and Planets...1

The Earth, Moon and Sun are Spheres 3

The Movement of the Earth...5

The Movement of Other Planets 6

Changing Ideas About the Solar System..7

A Model Solar System (Mini-Project 1) 9

Section 2 — The Earth and Sun

Day and Night 12

Making a Shadow Clock (Mini-Project 2) 14

Section 3 — The Moon

Moons 18

The Movement of the Moon 19

The Moon's Cycle 20

Mixed Questions 22

Glossary...26

Answers to the questions are on the back of the Pull-out Poster in the centre of the book.

Published by CGP

Contributors
Katie Braid, Rachael Marshall, Sarah Pattison, Camilla Simson
With thanks to Charlotte Burrows and Jill Cousner for the proofreading.

ISBN: 978 1 78294 090 6

Clipart from Corel®
Printed by Elanders Ltd, Newcastle upon Tyne.
Based on the classic CGP style created by Richard Parsons.

Text, design, layout and original illustrations © Coordination Group Publications Ltd. (CGP) 2014
All rights reserved.

Photocopying this book is not permitted, even if you have a CLA licence.
Extra copies are available from CGP with next day delivery • 0800 1712 712 • www.cgpbooks.co.uk

The Sun and Planets

We live on a planet called the <u>Earth.</u> It is one of the planets going around the <u>Sun.</u>

1. (Circle) the right words in **bold** to make the sentences below correct:

   There are **six / eight** planets around our Sun.

   The Sun and planets make up the **solar / moon** system.

   The Sun is a large **moon / star** in the centre of the **planets / Earth.**

2. Which of the words on the **rocket** on the right are **planets** going around our Sun and which are **not**? Put the words into the right columns on this table. One has been done for you.

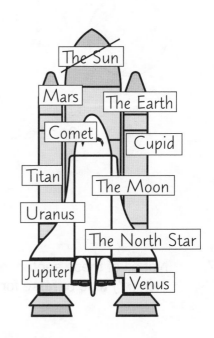

Planets	Not planets
	The Sun

3. Name **two** planets in our solar system that aren't mentioned in question 2.

   1. ....

   2. ....

4. Which planet is **closest** to the **Sun**? Put a tick (✔) in the box next to your answer.

   ☐ Earth   ☐ Neptune   ☐ Mercury

5. Why is it **dangerous** to look directly at the Sun?

   ....

   ....

© CGP — not to be photocopied

The Sun and Planets

6. This is a picture of our solar system.
    Write in the missing **names of the planets**. Some have been done for you.

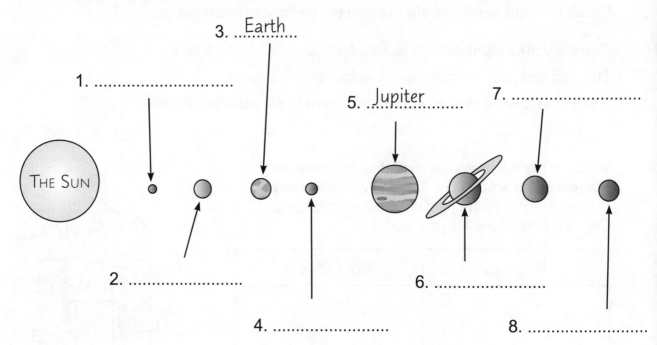

3. Earth

1. ....

5. Jupiter

7. ....

THE SUN

2. ....

6. ....

4. ....

8. ....

7. Not all of these sentences about the solar system are correct.
    Tick (✔) **true** or **false** for each one.

	TRUE	FALSE
Mercury is a planet.	☐	☐
There are no stars in our solar system.	☐	☐
Pluto is a planet.	☐	☐
Earth is the only planet with a moon.	☐	☐
Jupiter is the biggest planet.	☐	☐

INVESTIGATE

Look in a book or on the Internet to find out up to five facts about each planet. Use those facts to make a leaflet about our solar system. Include a picture of each planet.

  © CGP — not to be photocopied

The Earth, Moon and Sun are Spheres

Some things (like pancakes) are round but <u>flat</u> — others (like balls) are round <u>whichever</u> way you look at them. The special word for ball-shaped things is '<u>sphere</u>'.

1. (Circle) the right words in these sentences.

   If you look at a coin from the top, it looks **round / square** , but if you look at it from the side,

   it just looks like a **triangle / thin line** . This is because it's **round / flat** . A football

   is different. A football looks **flat / round** no matter which way you turn it.

   Instead of saying 'football-shaped', scientists use the fancy word **spherical / cuboid** .

2. Some of the things in this table are **flat**, and some are **spherical**. Finish off the table by writing 'flat' or 'spherical' underneath each picture.

   The Earth and the Moon and the Sun are kind of spherical. But they're not <u>perfect</u> spheres — they're only <u>roughly</u> ball-shaped.

Object	Earth	Ping pong ball	Coin	Moon	CD	Sun
Picture						
Flat or Spherical?						

3. Fill in the blanks in these sentences. Choose the right words from the box below.
   (You don't need to use all the words.)

   We can't tell just by .... on it that the Earth is spherical. It's

   only in the last 40 years that .... could be taken of the Earth

   from .... , but we have known for much longer than 40 years

   that the Earth is ....

flat	aliens	photographs
space	spherical	standing

© CGP — not to be photocopied   *Section 1 — The Solar System*

The Earth, Moon and Sun are Spheres

4. People used to believe the Earth was **flat**. Read the sentences below and decide which sentences are evidence to support the Earth being **flat**, which are evidence to support the earth being a **sphere**, and which are **not evidence** for either.

| We can see that the Earth is spherical from satellite photos. |

| No-one has fallen off the Earth and people think that someone would have if the Earth was a sphere. |

| The Earth feels flat and looks flat when we stand on it. |

| Astronauts went to the Moon and saw that the Earth is spherical. |

| It used to be impossible to go to the Moon. |

| Ships can sail right around the Earth. |

| The Moon looks like a sphere. |

Put each of the sentences into a column of the table to show which idea it supports.

Supports the Earth Being Flat	Supports the Earth Being a Sphere	Not Evidence for Either Idea

INVESTIGATE

· *Have a look around your house or classroom for objects that are spheres and objects that are*
· *round and flat. Make a table for the things you find, with spherical objects in one column, and*
· *round and flat objects in the other. Which of the spherical objects are not perfect spheres?*

  © CGP — not to be photocopied

The Movement of the Earth

The Earth goes round the Sun again, and again, and again — this is called <u>orbiting</u>.

1. Complete these sentences about the Earth's movement around the Sun.

    The Earth's path around the Sun is called its ....

    It's roughly in the shape of a ....

2. The picture below shows the Earth orbiting the sun. The arrows show how far
    the Earth has travelled round the sun at different times of the year. Draw and
    label three more arrows to show where the Earth will be in **April**, **July** and **October**.

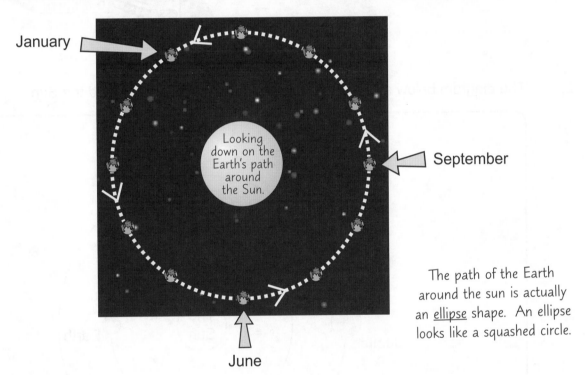

January

Looking
down on the
Earth's path
around
the Sun.

September

June

The path of the Earth
around the sun is actually
an <u>ellipse</u> shape. An ellipse
looks like a squashed circle.

3. How many **months** does it take the Earth to go round the Sun once?   ....

    How many **years** does it take?   ....

    How many **days** does it take?   ....

4. The Earth starts its orbit in **January**.
    In which month is it half way round the Sun?   ....

<u>*INVESTIGATE*</u> •

*Work out how many times the Earth goes around the Sun in 24 months. What about in
72 months? How many weeks does it take for the Earth to go round the Sun?*

© CGP — not to be photocopied   *Section 1 — The Solar System*

The Movement of Other Planets

While the Earth moves around the Sun, the <u>other planets</u> are moving too.

1. Use words from the **planet** to help you complete these sentences.

    All the planets in the solar system are

    orbiting .... Like the Earth,

    the orbits of the other planets are roughly

    .... Planets that

    are further from the sun have to travel

    .... to do one orbit.

    the Sun · square · each other · further · superglue · circular · less · the Earth

2. The diagram below shows the orbits of Jupiter and Earth around the Sun.

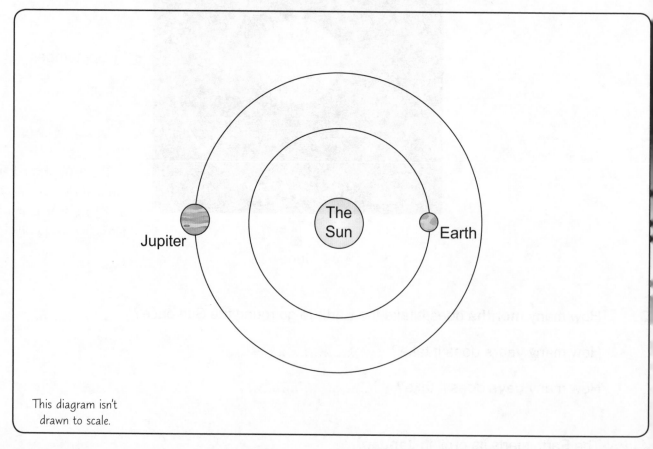

This diagram isn't drawn to scale.

Jupiter — The Sun — Earth

On the diagram, draw the orbits of **Mercury** and **Saturn**. Label the planets you've drawn.

INVESTIGATE ....

:   *Draw a larger version of the diagram in question 2 and complete it by filling in the rest*
:   *of the planets and their orbits. Which planet has the furthest to travel to orbit the Sun?*

Changing Ideas About the Solar System

In the past, people thought that the <u>Earth</u> was the <u>centre</u> of the solar system. They thought that the Sun, the Moon, all the other planets and all the other stars <u>orbited it.</u>

1. A scientist called **Ptolemy** observed that if you sit outside all night, the stars seem to move across the sky, like this.

Early in the evening the star is here....

... late at night it has moved over here.

Why might Ptolemy think this was evidence that the **Earth** was the **centre** of the solar system and everything else orbited it? Circle your answer.

Because it looks like the stars are going round the Earth.

Because it looks like the stars are far away.

Because you can see the stars all night.

2. Over a **thousand years** after Ptolemy died, a scientist called **Copernicus** came up with a different explanation for why the stars seemed to move. Circle his explanation below.

The stars are going around the moon.

The stars stay in one place but the Earth is moving.

The stars are moving further away.

Who do scientists today agree with — **Ptolemy** or **Copernicus**? ....

3. Look at the scientists below.

The Sun is at the centre of the solar system.

Everything in the solar system orbits the Earth.

Copernicus

Ptolemy

A scientist called **Galileo** discovered that there were **moons orbiting Jupiter**. Which of the scientists above did he prove wrong? ....

Give a reason for your answer. ....

....

© CGP — not to be photocopied

Changing Ideas About the Solar System

4. Over time, our ideas about the solar system **changed**.
Here are two different ideas about how the solar system is arranged.

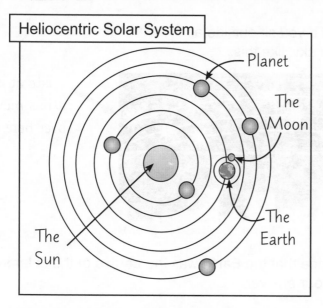

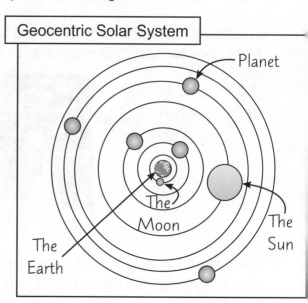

Which of the pictures above shows what scientists today think our solar system looks like?
Write **heliocentric** or **geocentric**.

....

5. Tick (✔) the sentence below that describes a **geocentric** solar system.

| The Earth orbits the Sun. | The Sun orbits the Earth. | The Earth orbits the Moon. |

6. Write down **two differences** between the heliocentric and geocentric ideas.

1. ....

....

2. ....

....

INVESTIGATE ●

Ptolemy lived from AD 90 to 168 and Copernicus lived from 1473 to 1543. Do you think it was easy or difficult for them to collect evidence of what the solar system looked like? Why? Do you think that it's easier or harder for scientists to collect evidence today?

● ●

 © CGP — not to be photocopied

A Model Solar System

The planets are really <u>big</u>, and it's a very long way between them. In this mini-project you're going to make a <u>model</u> of the solar system — a model is a <u>smaller version</u> of the real thing.

You will need this equipment to make your model:

Equipment:	
A big room, or space outside.	Nine different sized balls to be the Sun and planets.
A metre stick.	A calculator.
Sticky labels.	A pen or a pencil.

1. Where would it be sensible to look for information on the size of the planets? Put ticks (✔) in the boxes next to your answers.

   ☐ Any old page from the Internet.

   ☐ On the websites of museums and organisations that study space.

   ☐ In books about space.

   ☐ Ask your pet dog.

2. Here's a table showing the **size** of each planet from its centre to its surface (its radius). Write **1-8** in the last column to order the planets by size, starting with the **smallest**.

Planet	Radius (kilometres)	Order
Mercury	2440	
Venus	6052	
Earth	6371	
Mars	3390	
Jupiter	69 911	8
Saturn	58 232	
Uranus	25 362	
Neptune	24 622	

This one has been done for you.

MINI-PROJECT

A Model Solar System

3.   The Sun has a radius of 695 000 km. Is this **bigger** or **smaller** than the largest planet?

....

Now you need to **label** your planets. Follow the instructions below.

> *If you can't find 9 different sized balls, you can make some out of scrunched up paper or paper mache.*

1)   Put the nine balls in order from smallest to largest.
2)   Label the largest ball as the Sun.
3)   The rest of the balls are the planets. Label each one, using the table on page 9 to help you.

> *HINT: think about the <u>order</u> of the planets from the sun*

4.   This table shows **how far** each of the planets is from the Sun.
     Complete the **first column** by filling in the rest of the planets.

Planet	Distance from the Sun (kilometres)	Distance from the Sun in the model (centimetres)
Mercury	60 000 000	6
	110 000 000	
Earth	150 000 000	
Mars	230 000 000	23
	780 000 000	
	1 430 000 000	
Uranus	2 870 000 000	287
	4 500 000 000	

5.   Complete the **third column** of the table to show how far each planet should be from the Sun
     in your model. Do this by **dividing** the distances from the Sun by **10 000 000**.
     (This means that every 10 000 000 km in real life will be represented by 1 cm in your model.)

Once you've divided by 10 000 000, each number should have **7 fewer zeros**.

Some distances have been done for you.

          © CGP — not to be photocopied

A Model Solar System

Now you can make your model.

- Pick a place to put the object you want to be the **Sun**.
- Measure **6 cm** away from the Sun and place the ball labelled '**Mercury**' there.
- Look at your table to see how far **Venus** should be from the Sun.
  Measure that distance and put the ball labelled '**Venus**' there.
- Now do the same for the **other planets**.

Your planets may not fit in a straight line, you may have to put them in different places in their orbits.

Models can be pretty useful — sometimes it's easier to work things out by **looking** at something, rather than having to just **think** about it, especially if you have to think about big numbers.

6. Look at your model.
   Where is the **biggest** gap between two planets that are next to each other in your **model**?

   Between .... and ....

   What does that tell you about the gaps between the planets in the **solar system**?

   ....

   ....

7. How does the distance between the planets change as the distance from the Sun increases?

   ....

   ....

8. Could you use your model to answer questions about the **size** of the planets? ....

   Explain your answer.

   ....

   ....

EXTRA PROJECT
The radius of the moon is 1700 km and its distance from the Earth is about 400, 000 km. Use this information to add the Moon to your model.

© CGP — not to be photocopied   *Section 1 — The Solar System*

Section 2 — The Earth and Sun

Day and Night

The Sun <u>rises</u> every morning and <u>sets</u> every night, which makes it <u>look</u> as if it's moving around the Earth. But it's really the <u>Earth</u> that's <u>spinning</u>.

1.   Fill in the gaps to explain how the Earth **moves**. Pick the right words from the night sky.

The Earth is .... This means

it's spinning. It rotates ....

every day. The Sun .... where

it is. We can only .... the Sun when

our side of the Earth is facing the right way. It's .... when we're

facing the Sun and it's night time when we're facing .... from the Sun.

rotating   away   dangerous
Sun
see   stays   Earth
towards   daytime   once

2.   The sentences below are about things **moving**. Tick (✔) the sentences that are **true**.

☐   If you're on a train, it looks like all the trees and houses go whizzing past you. The train is standing still and the trees and houses are moving.

☐   If you're on a train, it looks like all the trees and houses go whizzing past you. The train is moving and the trees and houses are standing still.

☐   If you're on a roundabout, it looks like the rest of the world is spinning past. The roundabout is moving and the playground is staying still.

☐   If you're on the Earth, it looks like the Sun is going round the Earth, but it's not really moving. It's the Earth that's spinning.

☐   If you're on the Earth, it looks like the Sun rises and falls every day. The Sun is moving around the Earth.

                  © CGP — not to be photocopied

Answers to Y5 'Earth & Space'

3. E.g. the stick part is called the gnomon / if you move a shadow clock to another part of the Earth, it will show a different time / a sundial has to face the right way or it won't tell the time properly.

4. 3 o'clock
Day time. If it was night time there would be no sunlight and so no shadow would be made.

5. The sundial is in the shade, so there's no shadow.
It's cloudy, so there's no shadow.

6. Andre

7. important, not important, important, important

8. In the playground. In the park. In your garden.
E.g. there's not enough sunlight indoors so there won't be a shadow.

9.
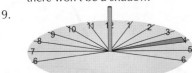

10. The Earth is rotating so the Sun seems to shine from different positions in the sky through the day. The straw stays in the same place on the Earth so the direction of its shadow changes.

11. If your shadow clock is in the same position, the answer should be no.

12. It's the same every day.

Section 3 — The Moon

Page 18 — Moons

1. A roughly spherical object that orbits a planet.

2.
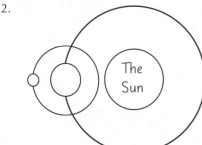

The Sun

3. only, more than, telescope, Jupiter, large, smaller, evidence, the Earth

Page 19 — The Movement of the Moon

1. 28 days, around, rotates, always

2.

3. A — false   B — true   C — true   D — false

Pages 20-21 — The Moon's Cycle

1. new, full, new

2. The full Moon stage — because you would be able to see all of the face of the moon.
The new Moon stage — because you would not be able to see the face of the moon at all.

3. The binoculars and telescope should be ticked.

4. Clouds.

5. smaller, bigger

6. the whole, crescent, full moon, 28 days

7. true, false, false, true
E.g. we can see the moon because the Sun shines on it / the Moon appears to change shape because parts of it don't get any light from the Sun.

Mixed Questions — Pages 22-25

1. tennis ball, Sun, Moon, orange

2. Freddy
day time
New Zealand
not

3. It would move.

4. A moon orbits a planet, not the Sun.
Jupiter has more than one moon.
A moon is a celestial body.

5. Uranus — 7, Venus — 2, Mars — 4, Neptune — 8, Jupiter — 5, Earth — 3, Saturn — 6

6. rotates, Sun, still

7.
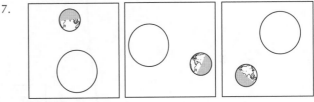

24, 365, year

8. circle / ellipse / oval

9. Earth, full, always, spins
about 28 days

10. true, false, true, true, false
E.g. The planets orbit the Sun / the Sun is a large star.

11. 12 months
The length of time it takes the Earth to orbit the Sun.

12. Any two of these: when it's cloudy, when it's night-time, when it's indoors, when it's in the shade, when it's facing the wrong way.

13. The sun / stars appearing to move across the sky.
The Earth is spinning and the sun and stars stay in the same place.
E.g. Copernicus, Galileo

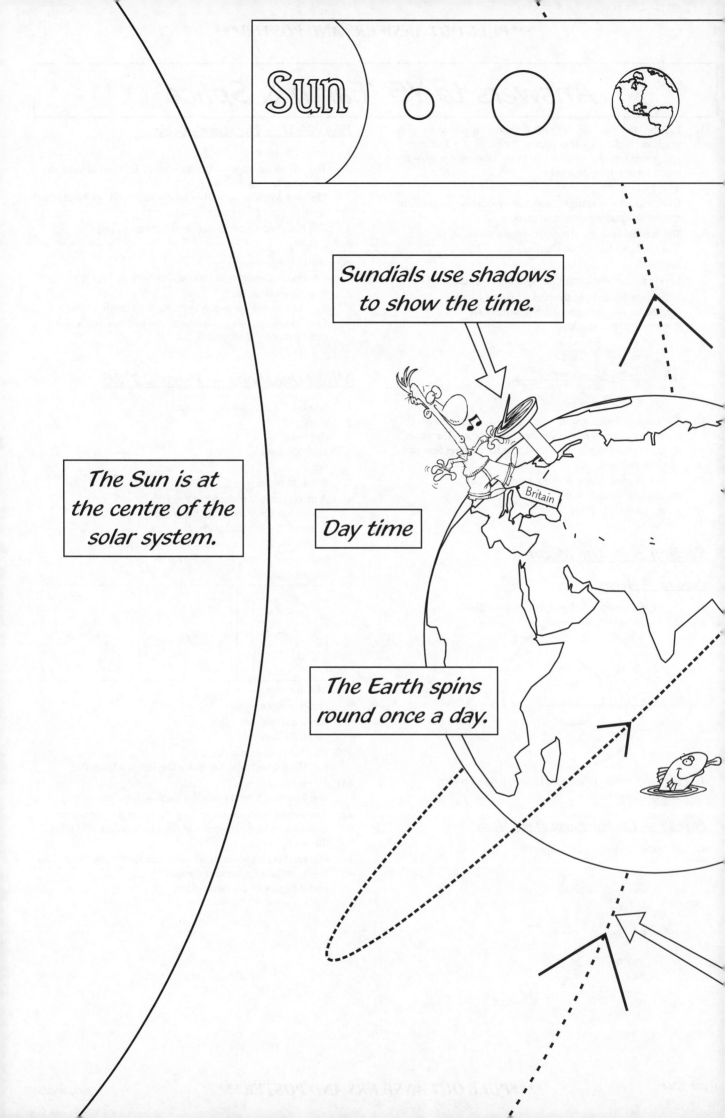

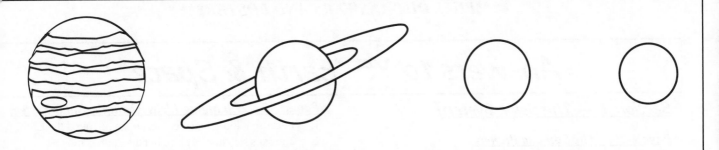

The moon orbits
the Earth.

Night time

EARTH
&
SPACE

Earth
the Sun.

Answers to Y5 'Earth & Space'

Section 1 — The Solar System

Page 1-2 — The Sun and Planets

1. These words should be circled: eight, solar, star, planets.
2. Planets: Mars, the Earth, Uranus, Jupiter, Venus.
   Not Planets: Comet, Cupid, Titan, the Moon, the North Star.
3. Mercury, Saturn, Neptune
4. Mercury
5. Because you might damage your eyes.
6. 1 – Mercury, 2 – Venus, 4 – Mars, 6 – Saturn, 7 – Uranus, 8 – Neptune.
7. true, false, false, false, true

Pages 3-4 — The Earth, Moon and Sun are Spheres

1. These words should be circled: round, thin line, flat, round, spherical.
2. Reading across the table: spherical, spherical, flat, spherical, flat, spherical.
3. standing, photographs, space, spherical
4. Supports the Earth being flat:
   The Earth feels flat and looks flat when we stand on it. No-one has fallen off the Earth and people think that someone would have if the Earth was a sphere.
   Supports the Earth being a sphere:
   Astronauts went to the Moon and saw that the Earth is spherical. Ships can sail right around the Earth. We can see that the Earth is spherical from satellite photos.
   Doesn't support either:
   It used to be impossible to go to the Moon.
   The Moon looks like a sphere.

Page 5 — The Movement of the Earth

1. orbit, circle
2.

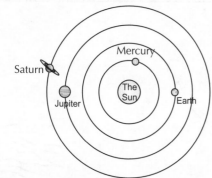

April ▷ ◁ October

◁ July

3. 12, 1, 365
4. July

Page 6 — The Movement of Other Planets

1. the Sun, circular, further
2.

Mercury
The Sun
Earth
Jupiter
Saturn

Pages 7-8 — Changing Ideas About the Solar System

1. Because it looks like the stars are going round the Earth.
2. The stars stay in one place but the Earth is moving.
   Copernicus
3. Ptolemy
   He showed that not everything orbits round the Earth.
4. Heliocentric
5. The Sun orbits the Earth.
6. E.g. In the heliocentric system the sun is in the centre and in the geocentric system the Earth is in the centre.
   In the heliocentric system moons orbit planets and in the geocentric system moons orbit around the centre (like all the planets).

Pages 9-11 — A Model Solar System

1. In books on space, on the websites of museums and organisations that study space.
2. From the top: 1, 3, 4, 2, 8, 7, 6, 5
3. bigger
4, 5.

Planet	Distance from the Sun in the Solar System (kilometres)	Distance from the Sun in the model (centimetres)
Mercury	60 000 000	6
Venus	110 000 000	11
Earth	150 000 000	15
Mars	230 000 000	23
Jupiter	780 000 000	78
Saturn	1 430 000 000	143
Uranus	2 870 000 000	287
Neptune	4 500 000 000	450

6. Between Neptune and Uranus.
   E.g. the biggest distance between two planets in the solar system is between Neptune and Uranus.
7. The distance between the planets increases as the distance from the Sun increases.
8. E.g. Yes. You ordered the balls for your model from smallest to largest and matched them to the size order of the planets.
   OR No. You didn't make the balls to scale.

Section 2 — The Earth and Sun

Pages 12-13 — Day and Night

1. rotating, once, stays, see, daytime, away
2. The second, third and fourth sentences should be ticked.
3. Bert — B, Rodney — A and C
4. day time, night time
5. night time, night time
6. going to bed

Pages 14-17 — Making a Shadow Clock

1. The box on the right should be ticked.
2. Sundials were used by the ancient Greeks — C
   A stick in the ground can be used as a simple shadow clock — A
   Ancient Egyptians used big stone pillars to tell the time — B
   The stick or pillar blocks the sunlight.

Day and Night

3. The pictures below show Rodney in Britain and Bert in Australia at different times of the day.

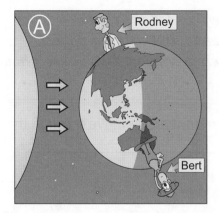 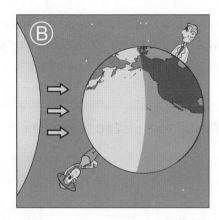 

Which picture shows **Bert's** day time? ....

Which pictures show **Rodney's** day time? .... and ....

4. Fill in the blanks with the correct words from the brackets.

Rodney's .... (day time / night time) is when Britain is facing the Sun

and his .... (day time / night time) is when Britain is not facing the Sun.

5. Fill in the blanks with either **day time** or **night time**.

When it's day time for Rodney in Britain, it's .... for Bert in Australia.

When it's day time for Bert in Australia, it's .... for Rodney in Britain.

6. In picture A it has just become light for Rodney.
   Is Bert **getting up** in the morning, or is he **going to bed**?

   ....

INVESTIGATE

Use the Internet to find out what time it is in different countries round the world. Make a table with three columns. Write the name of each country in the first column and the time it is there in the second column. In the third column say whether it is day or night.

© CGP — not to be photocopied   *Section 2 — The Earth and Sun*

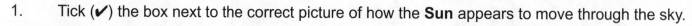

MINI-PROJECT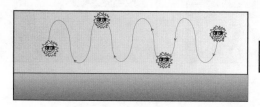

Making a Shadow Clock

> *Shadows change during the day, so you can use them to tell the time.*
> *People have used shadow clocks for thousands of years. In this mini-project,*
> *you'll make your own shadow clock by marking where a shadow falls at each hour.*

1. Tick (✔) the box next to the correct picture of how the **Sun** appears to move through the sky.

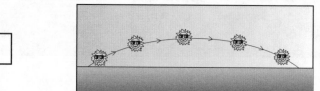

2. The sentences below describe some different types of **shadow clocks**.
   Draw lines to match each sentence to the picture of the shadow clock it is describing.

   Sundials were
   used by the
   ancient Greeks.

   A stick in the ground
   can be used as a
   simple shadow clock.

   Ancient Egyptians
   used big stone pillars
   to tell the time.

   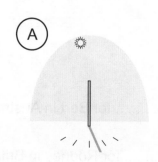 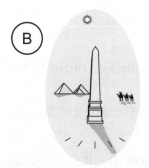 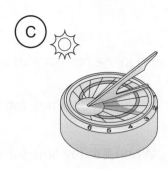

   How are the shadows **made** on the shadow clocks?

   ....

3. Find a book or a website about **sundials** and **shadow clocks**.
   Write down **one** interesting fact about them that isn't in question 2.

   ....

   ....

          © CGP — not to be photocopied

Making a Shadow Clock

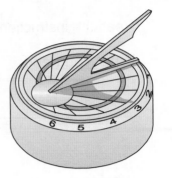

MINI-PROJECT

4. Look at the sundial on the right.

What **time** is it showing? .... o' clock

Is it **day time** or **night time**? ....

Explain your answer. ....

....

....

5. Frank has problems with his sundial.
For each picture, write down why Frank **can't** tell the time.

....

....

....

....

....

....

6. The picture on the right is of the **Eiffel Tower** in France.

Ricci thinks the Eiffel Tower could be used as a shadow clock at any time.
Andre thinks it could be used as a shadow clock, but only on sunny days.
Ant doesn't think it could be used as a shadow clock at all.

Who is right? (Circle) the right answer.

Ricci   Andre   Ant

© CGP — not to be photocopied

MINI-PROJECT

Making a Shadow Clock

Read the instructions below that describe how to make a shadow clock.

<u>What you need:</u>

straw

paper plate

| A paper plate. | A straw | A pen or pencil. |

You could use a stick or a pencil instead of a straw.

<u>What to do:</u>

12

1. Turn the paper plate upside down and write the number '12' on the edge.

2. Make a hole in the centre of the plate and push the straw through the hole. Make sure the straw is straight.

3. Draw a line from the 12 to the straw.

4. Check that it's a sunny day. If it is, put your shadow clock on the ground outside just before 12 o'clock (midday).

5. At 12 o'clock, turn the shadow clock so that the shadow of the straw lines up with the line you drew to the number 12.

6. At 1 o'clock, draw a line along the shadow of the straw. Write 1 where the line touches the edge of the plate.

7. Repeat drawing and labelling a line for each hour for the rest of the school day. Carry on for every hour in the morning on the next sunny school day.

7. Read each sentence below. For each one, tick (✔) the box to say if you think it is **important** or **not important** when you're making a shadow clock.

	Important	Not Important
The shadow clock is left in the same place.	☐	☐
The shadow clock is made on a weekday.	☐	☐
The straw is always in the same position.	☐	☐
The shadow clock is in a place with lots of sunshine.	☐	☐

Now follow the method above to make your shadow clock.

© CGP — not to be photocopied

Making a Shadow Clock

8. Circle the places that you could **use** a shadow clock.

In the classroom.   In the playground.   In the park.

In your garden.   In your bedroom.

Why **couldn't** you use a shadow clock in the other places?

....

9. Below is a completed shadow clock. **Draw** where the shadow will be at 4 o'clock.

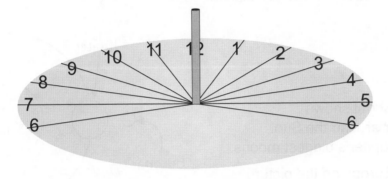

10. Why does the shadow **move**?

....

....

....

11. Draw a line along the shadow on your shadow clock at the end of your school day and label it. Check the position of the shadow when you leave school on the next day.

Has its position at the end of the day **changed**? ....

HINT: make sure your shadow clock is always in the same position.

12. What does your shadow clock tell you about the **path** the Sun seems to take through the sky? Circle the right answer.

It sometimes changes.   It's the same every day.   It changes every day.

EXTRA PROJECT

Some scientists think that Stonehenge is an example of an ancient clock or calendar. Look in a book or on the Internet to find out what Stonehenge looks like and how old scientists think it is. Why do they think it was used to tell the time of year?

© CGP — not to be photocopied

Section 3 — The Moon

Moons

A moon is an <u>object</u> in space that <u>orbits a planet</u>. We call Earth's moon 'the Moon', but it's not the only one — <u>other planets</u> have moons too.

1. Tick (✔) the sentence below that describes a **moon**.

   ☐ A roughly spherical object that orbits the sun.

   ☐ A roughly spherical object that orbits a planet.

   ☐ A planet that orbits another planet.

   A moon is a <u>celestial body</u>. This means it's something in the sky that hasn't been made by humans.

2. The picture on the right shows the orbit of **Jupiter** around the Sun. Europa is one of Jupiter's biggest moons.

   Draw the orbit of Europa on the picture.

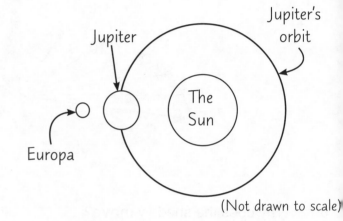

   Jupiter · Jupiter's orbit · The Sun · Europa

   (Not drawn to scale)

3. Complete the sentences below, using the words on the **moons** to help you.

   Earth has .... one moon but other planets have

   .... one. We can use a ....

   to see the moons of other planets. .... has four

   .... moons and lots of .... ones.

   When scientists discovered that other planets had moons it was

   .... that not everything in our solar system

   orbits around ....

   more than · Jupiter · the Earth · evidence · telescope · large · only · smaller

---

INVESTIGATE . . . .

- *Use books or the Internet to find out how many moons each planet has. Put your results in a table with two columns — put the planet's name in one column and the number of moons in the other. Which planet has the fewest moons? Which planet has the most?*

. . . .

     © CGP — not to be photocopied

The Movement of the Moon

As the Moon orbits the Earth, it spins so that the <u>same</u> side always faces the Earth.

1. Ⓒircle the right words in the brackets to complete this information about the **Moon**.

   It takes about (**28 days** / **4 days**) for the Moon to orbit the Earth. Orbit means
   to go (**through** / **around**) something. As the moon moves around the Earth
   it (**rotates** / **flips**) so that we (**always** / **usually**) see the same side from Earth.

2. It's the year 2090 and Helen has gone to the **Moon** for a holiday.
   When she lands her rocket, she can't see the Earth. She walks
   around the Moon to the side that is facing the Earth, like this:

   She decides to stay on that side.
   This picture shows **six stages**
   of the Moon's orbit.

   Draw Helen and her rocket
   in the right place on the blank
   Moons to complete the picture.

   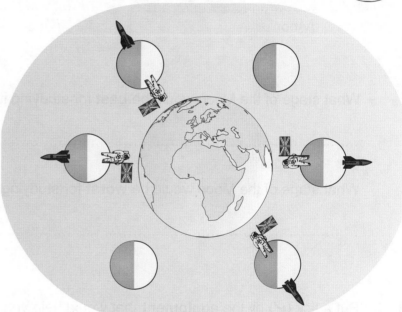

3. Decide whether these sentences are **true** or **false** and cross out the wrong choice.

   Ⓐ Helen can only see the Earth for half the Moon's orbit.
   Ⓑ In all of the pictures, Helen can see the Earth.
   Ⓒ You would never be able to see the rocket from the Earth.
   Ⓓ If you looked through a powerful telescope, you would see the rocket.

INVESTIGATE

*Get a friend to stand in a space in the playground or classroom and pretend to be the
Earth. You are the moon. Move around your friend like the moon orbiting the Earth —
make sure that you're always facing them. See if you can do one orbit in exactly 28 steps.*

© CGP — not to be photocopied   *Section 3 — The Moon*

The Moon's Cycle

The Moon's cycle is the 28 days from <u>new Moon</u> to the next <u>new Moon</u>. During this cycle, it looks like it's <u>changing shape</u> because parts of the moon don't get any <u>light</u> from the Sun.

1. Use the descriptions of full Moon and new Moon to write **full** or **new** in the blanks below.

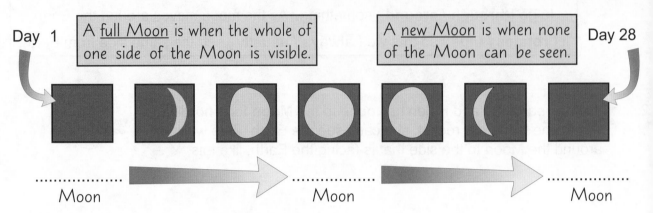

Day 1 | A <u>full Moon</u> is when the whole of one side of the Moon is visible. | A <u>new Moon</u> is when none of the Moon can be seen. | Day 28

Moon   Moon   Moon

2. What stage of the Moon would be **best** for studying it? Why?

    ....

    What stage of the Moon would be **worst** for studying it? Why?

    ....

3. Put a tick (✔) by the **equipment** that would help you see the Moon's surface.

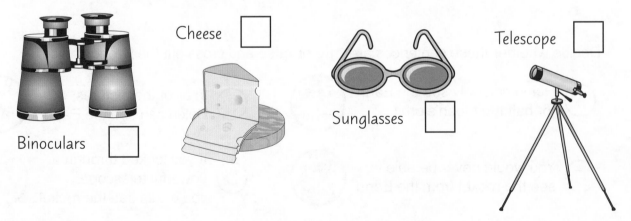

Cheese ☐

Telescope ☐

Sunglasses ☐

Binoculars ☐

4. You want to study the Moon tonight, and it's at the best stage for studying it. What might **stop** you being able to see the Moon?

    ....

     © *CGP — not to be photocopied*

The Moon's Cycle

5. Say whether the Moon appears to be getting **bigger** or **smaller** after a full Moon and after a new Moon.

    Just after a full Moon: ....

    Just after a new Moon: ....

6. (Circle) the right words to complete these sentences about the **stages of the Moon**.

    A full Moon is when (**the whole** / **72%**) of one side of the Moon can be seen.

    After a full Moon, the area we can see gets smaller. It looks (**carrot** / **crescent**) shaped.

    When we can't see it at all, it's called a new Moon. Then it appears to grow bigger until

    there is another (**full moon** / **planet**). The Moon takes approximately

    (**28 years** / **28 days**) to go from one new Moon to the next.

7. Write **true** or **false** after each of these sentences.

    The Moon's cycle is about 28 days long.   ....

    We can see the Moon because it gives off light, like the Sun.   ....

    The Moon changes shape because it gets bigger and smaller.   ....

    Even when you can't see the moon, it is still there.   ....

    Choose **one** of the sentences that you've marked as false and rewrite it so that it's **correct**.

    ....

    ....

INVESTIGATE . . . .

Have a look at the moon every night for the next four weeks. Make a chart of the moon's
cycle by drawing the shape of the moon each night on a calendar or a grid labelled with
the days of the month. Can you predict when the next full and new moon will be?

© CGP — not to be photocopied   *Section 3 — The Moon*

Mixed Questions

Don't space out just yet. It's time to <u>check</u> what you've <u>learned</u> about the Sun, the Moon and the planets by having a go at these questions.

1. (Circle) the things below that have a roughly **spherical** shape.

   pancake   tennis ball   pencil   elephant   orange

        tea cup   Sun   plate   Moon

2. Here's a picture of Freddy in France and Neil in New Zealand.

   Who's on the side of the Earth **facing** the Sun? ....

   Is Freddy in **day time** or **night time**? ....

   Is it **night time** in France or New Zealand? ....

   Is New Zealand **facing** the Sun or not? ....

3. If you stood still in your garden for a whole day, would your shadow point in the **same direction** or would it **move** throughout the day?

   ....

4. Tick (✔) any of the sentences below that are correct.

   ☐ All planets have one moon.   ☐ A moon orbits a planet, not the Sun.   ☐ Earth is the only planet with a moon.

   ☐ Jupiter has more than one moon.   ☐ A moon is a celestial body.

     © CGP — not to be photocopied

Mixed Questions

Write the numbers **1-8** in the boxes to put the planets in order of **distance** from the Sun, starting with the closest. I've done the first one for you.

[ ] Uranus   [ ] Venus   [ ] Mars   [ ] Neptune

[1] Mercury   [ ] Jupiter   [ ] Earth   [ ] Saturn

Finish the sentences by choosing the right words from the box.

The Earth .... once each day.

This makes the .... seem to move through the sky.

But the Sun actually stays ....

still	Earth
rotates	Sun

7. Look at the pictures below. In each picture, **shade in** the part of the Earth that is in darkness. Then complete the sentences in the box below.

The Earth rotates once every .... hours.

It takes .... days for the Earth to orbit the Sun once.

This is the same as one ....

8. What is the **shape** of the Earth's orbit? ....

© CGP — not to be photocopied   *Mixed Questions*

Mixed Questions

9. Complete these sentences about the **moon** by choosing the correct words from the brackets

The Moon orbits the .... (Earth / Sun). When we can see

the whole side of the Moon we call it a .... (new / full) Moon.

The same side of the Moon .... (always / sometimes)

faces the Earth. This is because the Moon .... (spins / hides)

while it moves around the Earth.

How many **days** are there between full moons? ....

10. Tick (✔) the sentences below that are **true** and cross (✗) the sentences that are **false**.

There are eight planets in our solar system.	☐
The planets orbit the Earth.	☐
The Moon orbits the Earth.	☐
The Earth is closer to the Moon than the Sun	☐
The Sun is a large planet.	☐

Choose **one** sentence that you marked as false and **rewrite** it so that it's correct.

....

....

                                                    © CGP — not to be photocopied

Mixed Questions

11.   How long is a **year**? Choose the **two** right answers and write them out on the lines below.

The length of time it takes the Moon to orbit the Earth.

12 months.

The length of time it takes the Sun to orbit the Moon.

3 seasons.

12 seasons.

10 months.

The length of time it takes the Earth to orbit the Sun.

24 months.

1. ....

....

2. ....

....

12.   Give **two** examples of when you **can't** use a sundial to tell the time.

1. ....

2. ....

13.   Nearly 2000 years ago, a scientist called Ptolemy thought that the **Earth** was the centre of our solar system. What could he **see** that made him think that?

....

....

Write down a **different** explanation for what Ptolemy could see.

....

....

Name **one** scientist that thought that the **Sun** was the centre of our solar system.

....

Glossary

Celestial body	A **natural** object that is in the **sky**. For example, moons and planets.
Copernicus	A scientist who believed the **Sun** was the centre of the solar system.
Ellipse	A shape that looks like a squashed circle.
Full Moon	When the **whole** of one side of the Moon can be seen from Earth.
Geocentric model	A model of the solar system that has the **Earth** in the centre.
Heliocentric model	A model of the solar system that has the **Sun** in the centre.
Moon	An **object** that orbits a planet. Different planets have different numbers of moons.
New Moon	When **none** of the Moon can be seen from Earth.
Orbit	The **path** an object takes **around another object** in space. It's also the **movement** of the object round another object.
Planet	A large, spherical object that orbits a **star**. There are **eight** planets in our solar system.
Ptolemy	A scientist who believed the **Earth** was the centre of the solar system.
Solar system	The **Sun** and the things that **orbit it**, including **Earth** and the other **planets**.
Spherical	Shaped like a **ball**.
Sun	A large **star** in the **centre** of our solar system.
Sundial	An early clock that shows the **time** using the direction of a **shadow**.

© *CGP — not to be photocopied*